DOUBTFUL TALES DOUBTFUL TALES
DOUBTFUL TALES DOUBTFUL TALES
DOUBTFUL TALES DOUBTFUL TALES
DOUBTFUL TALES DOUBTFUL TALES
DOUBTFUL TALES DOUBTFUL TALES
DOUBTFUL TALES DOUBTFUL TALES
DOUBTFUL TALES DOUBTFUL TALES
DOUBTFUL TALES DOUBTFUL TALES
DOUBTFUL TALES DOUBTFUL TALES
DOUBTFUL TALES DOUBTFUL TALES
DOUBTFUL TALES DOUBTFUL TALES
DOUBTFUL TALES DOUBTFUL TALES
DOUBTFUL TALES DOUBTFUL TALES
DOUBTFUL TALES DOUBTFUL TALES

DOUBTFUL TALES DOUBTFUL TALES
DOUBTFUL TALES DOUBTFUL TALES
DOUBTFUL TALES DOUBTFUL TALES
DOUBTFUL TALES DOUBTFUL TALES
DOUBTFUL TALES DOUBTFUL TALES
DOUBTFUL TALES DOUBTFUL TALES
DOUBTFUL TALES DOUBTFUL TALES
DOUBTFUL TALES DOUBTFUL TALES
DOUBTFUL TALES DOUBTFUL TALES
DOUBTFUL TALES DOUBTFUL TALES
DOUBTFUL TALES DOUBTFUL TALES
DOUBTFUL TALES DOUBTFUL TALES
DOUBTFUL TALES DOUBTFUL TALES
DOUBTFUL TALES DOUBTFUL TALES
DOUBTFUL TALES DOUBTFUL TALES

1st Edition

www.cvdarts.com
cvdarts@hotmail.com

Prolo....Prollogu...Beginning bit.

The tale you are about to read has been handed down from generation to generation. It's accuracy is certainly in question, but we think that on the whole it's probably nonsense. Phillatious Quill was born in Venice and became very good friends with Casanova. He certainly enjoyed all the fruits that several countries had to offer, but somehow always seemed to return to his home town. This is the rhyming text version of that incredible journey.

Final Warning
This really isn't for kids.

Dedicated to
Searchers of knowledge and
Historical events, fabricated within
The mind of
A nutter.

Phillatious Quill

Twas the year of our lord 1725,
When Phillatious our hero was born,
Twas in the romantic city of Venice,
On a sunny April Morn.

His Mum, Zanetta, was a talented Actress,
Who liked a good drink and a pill,
His Dad was a flexible, dandy dancer,
By the name of Lickerme Quill.

Phillatious Quill was the last of four,
His siblings were all in care,
His parents only had love for the stage,
And would share all their frilly underwear.

Now Venice was really the capital of fun,
Where to score you hardly need try,
And political religious conservatives,
Would certainly turn a blind eye.

They Permitted a whole host of Vices,
And games like 'Pepperoni Jock'
Where a pizza would duly be awarded,
To the man with the largest Cock.

They Encouraged all types of tourists,
To visit their land Day by Day,
And frequent the city's best brothels,
To see hookers and have it away.

When the famed carnival of Venice,
Ended with the first day of Lent,
The exciting Piazza San Marco,
Is the place where everyone went.

With ball gowns a plenty and elaborate masks,
A young man would turn to a hunter,
But of course the dangers of mask wearing girls,
Is the fact that you might get a munter.

The men would fill up their pants with socks,
To attract a naive young wench,
But later that night, she would get quite mad,
When she gave his goolies a clench.

They Called it a Grand Tour, back in the day,
When the English would travel abroad,
To find lots of Art and centres of culture,
And somewhere for dipping their sword.

It really was a City of fun,
With music and love in the air,
With gambling houses and courtesans cute,
And mistresses willing to share.

But what of our hero, the young Master Quill,
Whose arrival had been quite a quest,
Well Zanetta and Lickerme went acting again,
So they packed him off with the rest.

Phillatious was brought up by Nanny Balzari,
She taught him to read and to wash,
She really was a lovable Gal,
With a six inch, curly moustache.

At nine he was sent to a boarding house,
On the mainland town of Padua,
Put under the care of Guzzi the priest,
Whose intentions could not have been truer.

At 16 Phillatious moved in with the priest,
Whose wife was just like a mum,
Until the night she got smashed off her tits,
And put a finger, right up his bum.

Although Phillatious was certainly shocked,
It had kindled a feeling of pleasure,
And stirred his desires for a fancy life,
Of loving and music and leisure.

Unduly concerned for style and fashion,
Phillatious met new friends at Uni,
And roomed with a boy of similar tastes,
Who certainly seemed quite unruly.

"Casanova's the Name" began the young scamp,
"Studying philosophy, chemistry and law,
I'm also looking at medicine and maths,
But to be honest it's a bit of a bore."

"Hello" said Phillatious. Quill is my name,
"I'm also studying law,
But writing's the passion that floats my boat,
That and the mouth of a whore."

The two lads laughed like a couple of drains,
Casanova then started to drink,
"Then party we must" said the lovable rogue,
"Let's get wasted boy, what do you think?"

So for one or two years, they partied like kings,
With the wine and the ladies and song,
They gambled away and both got into debt,
But would never concede it was wrong.

Despite their behaviour they both got degrees,
And were able to practice in law,
They went back to Venice and started careers,
With the rich they had started to draw.

They gained a fine patron from a local Palazzo ,
Called Alvise Gaspero Malipiero,
A Venetian Senator of 76 years,
With the look of a Spanish caballero.

He moved in high circles and taught the young lads,
About food and great wines and behaviour,
They lived at the Palace and enjoyed all the fruits,
But the best one of all they would savour.

Alvise's intended was Teresa Imer,
A young Actress they spied on the gantry,
The boys would flatter and woo her until,
They could spit roast her down in the pantry.

When caught in the act, Alvise blew a fuse,
And fired them there on the spot,
They took all their clothes and what money they had,
And legged it before they were shot.

"Well that's disappointing" said Phillatious in rue,
And Casanova had to agree,
"Do you think that Alvise would have been so cross,
If Teresa had taken all three."

The lads found a hostel near Campo san Samuel,
The owner was Marco Savorgnan,
His daughter Nanetta was musically minded,
And certainly played the odd organ.

Her sister Maria was just as much fun,
And suggested the lads join their party,
They drank and they danced well into the night,
Till the gases had made them quite farty.

Avoiding the smell, they retired to a room,
Where the girls had decided to visit,
They started to fondle and clothes were removed,
Until things had became quite explicit.

The following morn with a smile and a wave,
The lads were off on their way,
They had a few drinks in a Venice Casino,
Then gambled the rest of the day.

They lived and they laughed with a drink and a bet,
Till their debts had started to climb,
And when they could no longer pay all the bills,
They were jailed for the very first time.

"We need to get jobs" said Casanova from the cell,
"I'm loving the life that we lead,
It's time to become quite noble and rich,"
And Phillatious duly agreed.

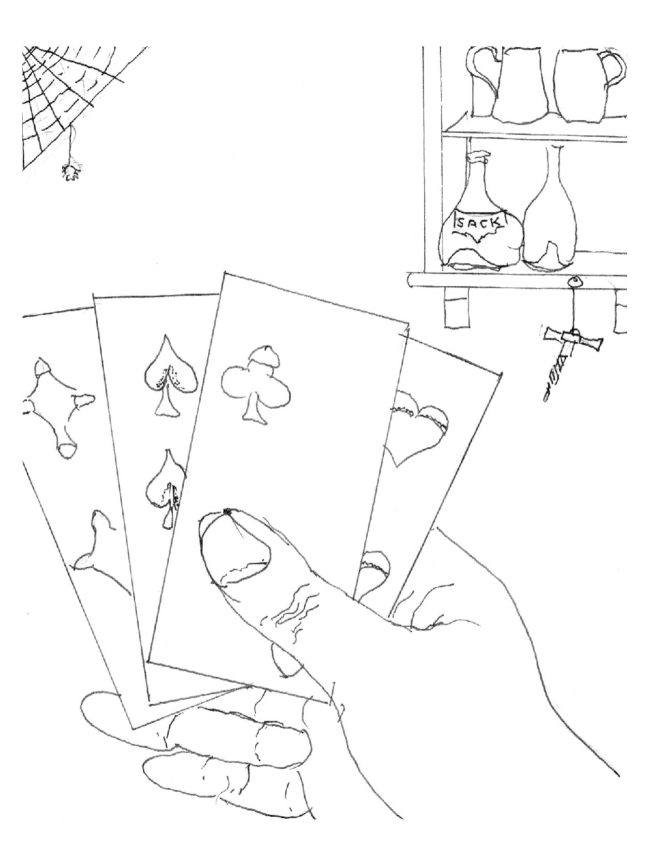

When once again free the lads found a job,
With the Cardinal Acquaviva in Rome,
They would write all his powerful letters of state,
And to girls who had polished his dome.

They met with the Pope and had pleaded to see,
The forbidden books in the vault,
The girl in the library was soon with child,
But the lads said it wasn't their fault.

They wrote for another but were caught in a scandal,
With some local lovers in clover,
Acquaviva fired them there on the spot,
And their church career was all over.

"Why does it always end up this way?"
Asked Casanova during one of his rants,
"It's really simple," said Phillatious with a grin,
"We can't keep our chaps in our pants."

"I know what to do" said Casanova with a smile,
"Why don't we both become soldiers,
We can buy commissions for the Republic of Venice,
And wear silver and gold on our shoulders!"

"We'll both have long swords and a cane in hand,
And a trim hat with a Cockade rosette,
Our hair will be perfumed with pigtail t'boot,
And to conquer the City we'd be set."

So a month from that day the lads were all set,
And commissions were bought in Corfu,
But within a few weeks the guys were bored,
So started a Card school in lieu.

Faro became the game they adored,
Where the banker would flip over suits,
If they matched the ones you held in your hand,
You would win it or soon lose your boots.

The lads soon realised they were lovers not fighters,
And the Military was not in their head,
So they gave it all up and returned to Venice,
To be professional gamblers instead.

They lost all the money from sale of commissions,
And were starting to feel in the poop,
But a dandy, Grimani, took pity on the lads,
And they joined his musical group.

Casanova had played the violin as a kid,
So his knowledge had developed some wealth,
But Phillatious had nothing, and felt like a man,
With no arms trying to play with himself.

"I could bang on a drum" said Phillatious in jest,
"At least I would stay on the listing,
Failing that I could visit your dandy Grimani,
And give him a jolly good fisting."

Casanova laughed loud as he gazed at his pal,
"I've got the whole matter in hand,
You can ding the triangle to the beat of the tune,
That will sure keep your placc in the band."

Phillatious was grateful and so the band played,
For the nobles and girls that were pretty,
They played in the theatre and many a ball,
And were banging all over the city.

The band were all jesters and snuck out at night,
And would play lots of practical jokes,
Like letting loose gondolas out on the water,
Or calling for doctors in hoax.

At one ball Phillatious had met a sweet girl,
But she had a great case of the shankles,
He tried to escape but he fell down the stairs,
With his pants tightly wrapped round his ankles.

At another he met a pretty young thing,
But between them too much they had drank,
The thought of performing was too much to bear,
So Phillatious had settled for a wank.

Casanova and Phillatious had played at a wedding,
And straight after had saved a fine bloke,
The Senator Bragadin, had been out on the water,
But sadly had suffered a stroke.

A physician was called and he bled the poor chap,
Which seemed to be taking it's time,
A mercury ointment was placed on his chest,
And his temperature started to climb.

The physician was angry and started to rage,
When Casanova had started to say,
"You're doing it wrong, this man has a fever,
You must take the ointment away."

Casanova stepped in and washed the man's chest,
The physician went off in a huff,
The Senator's temperature started to fall,
And he no longer felt really rough.

Phillatious was shocked by the skill of his friend,
As he stood there and drank from a Challis,
The friends of Bragadin were equally pleased,
And said he should live at the Palace.

Although feeling sad, Phillatious then said,
"You must take them up on their offer.
This is a chance for you to be rich,
Now come on lets go pack your koffer.

For three years Casanova lived at the palace,
Dressed well and spent lots of money,
While Phillatious had travelled up north to France,
In search of a life filled with honey.

One of his quests was Lilly Pongpois,
A blonde with a cute middle parting,
She had all the grace of a princess at large,
But sadly she couldn't stop farting.

On one night they tended a lavishing gala,
At the Palace de Chaffler de Nuts,
The nobles all noticed her unknown cologne,
But Lilly had just dropped her guts.

When bathing in oils and smiling so sweetly,
Phillatious had asked her to stay,
But reaching for the loofah, she left off a bazooka,
So Phillatious then called it a day.

He visited theatres and galleries galore,
And tasted much fruit on the way,
But one day he saw her, the girl of his dreams,
By the sweet name of Jodic Bouteille.

The house of Bouteille, was a fashionable one,
Where the dresses you never would hoick,
Though Jodie she cared for the loveable rogue,
He was viewed, as a bit of an oik.

"Tell me my fool" she would start her engage,
"What matters of state lie ahead?"
Phillatious had noticed her bosom of plenty,
And said "Let's discuss it in bed."

The Great Bed Of
SORROW

"I cannot consort with a social inept,"
Said Jodie adjusting her scarf,
"Though glancing upon your smallest of bulge,
I think I'd be in for a laugh."

"Oh let it be known" said Phillatious with aghast,
"I have satisfied Ladies of honour,"
"If believe that I must" said Jodie in brief,
"I would have to say, why would they bother?"

"I am known across Europe for the making of love,"
Said Phillatious with an eyebrow in height,
"Well that maybe so" came Jodie's retort,
"But you smell so I'll bid you goodnight."

Jodie then gracefully floated away,
While Phillatious examined his pits,
There wasn't a hint of the foulest B.O,
But the caviar had given him the shits.

"Oh bugger" he said as he awkwardly moved,
A restroom was now the agenda,
For though no one saw, you could see on his face,
That his blowhole was feeling quite tender.

After a clean he was back on top form,
And Jodie was high on his list,
He found her again, surrounded by men,
She was dancing and looking quite pissed.

Phillatious moved in and scared off the crowd,
While Jodie replenished her glass,
"Why thank you kind sir," she said with a smile,
"Now tell me, the state of your arse?"

Phillatious was smiling and led her away,
To the garden of fragrance and hues,
He looked quite impressed that a lady of note,
Seemed able to hold lots of booze.

"So tell me my lady" he said with a grin,
"Am I able to enchant your fair heart?"
"I'm not really sure" she replied with a smile,
But washing your bum was a start.

While Phillatious was busy with socials in France,
Casanova had come quite unstuck,
He had yet again upset a boss of good will,
And was clearly quite down on his luck.

His practical jokes had been met with distain,
And for ages he'd not won a bet,
So he fled to Palma and had an affair,
With a French woman called Henriette.

Like Phillatious, Casanova had struggled with class,
From his standing and pure lack of dosh,
Henriette was a lady of breeding and wealth,
And besides that, she wasn't half posh.

She soon called it quits and Casanova was crushed,
He had soon gotten used to the riches,
But sweet Henriette showed her class to the end,
Stuffing 500 coins in his britches.

So Casanova returned to his home town of Venice,
Where good gambling soon led him to tour,
With one or two friends, he headed to France,
Where he soon saw a face from before.

"Well hello Phillatious" said the rogue with a grin,
As he entered the room at a Ball,
Phillatious was stoked and hugged his dear friend,
Then gained the attention of all.

"Ladies and gentlemen this is my friend,
Casanova's the name you should know,
Lock up your daughters and lock up your wives,
It's time to get on with the show."

The gentlemen laughed with unease in their voice,
And girl's blushing had started to burst,
Especially when the loveable rogue,
Took his coat off and asked who was first.

So Philly and Cas were back in the game,
And laughter ensued in just minutes,
Then Phillatious, introduced Jodie to Cas,
But stated that she was off limits.

Phillatious and the lady had started to bond,
But they both knew it wasn't to be,
For the family Bouteille would never accept,
A rogue on the family tree.

So Philly and Cas then started to travel,
From one party town to another,
In Lyon they joined a freemason lodge,
Where everyone there was your brother.

They hung around Paris for a couple of years,
And were having the time of their lives,
But soon got in trouble with many a man,
For fooling around with their wives.

Their actions had often enraged the police,
And although the lads don't deserve pity,
Husbands and noblemen started to shout,
So the law drove them out of the city.

In the year of our lord, 1752
The two men were living in Dresden,
They entered the theatre and wrote a few plays,
But their topics were out of the question.

While there they soon came across Casanova's mum,
Who as usual could not give a toss,
But Casanova then wrote a well received play,
Which was aptly entitled, 'The Lost'.

The boys went to Prague, and Vienna was next,
But the morals were too tight to bare,
So they headed back home to their city of fun,
Back to Venice, and San Marco Square.

Phillatious was trying to avoid a big lump,
By the name of Francesca del Gannet,
She bounced in the room on the hunt for a groom,
With a belly the size of a planet.

"I want you Phillatious" She screamed with a snort,
From a hole in her fat cheesy face,
Phillatious was scared and ran for the door,
But the wobbler quite fancied a chase.

Meanwhile, Casanova had fallen for a man,
Bellino, the singer from the stalls,
In order to reach the very high notes,
The 'Castrata' would cut off their balls.

As it turned out Bellino was really a girl,
A secret Cas wouldn't divulge,
So he let people think he was wonderfully pink,
And his lover had once had a bulge.

But like many others the romance was short,
As fame came along for the singer,
And off she soon went on the trail of gold,
Leaving Cas with a very sore ringer.

For though a wee girl she loved all her toys,
With dildos you just couldn't fake it,
With all her strength she would thrust with her length,
And Cas, well he just had to take it.

They dressed very finely and moved in the circles,
Of noblemen, Royalty and priests,
But seemingly dubious actions when drunk,
Would lead to their banning from feasts.

At one point they entered the city cathedral,
Quite naked, and yelling out 'Knickers',
Phillatious himself had reached a new low,
When he flashed off his tap to the vicars.

Growing reports of naughty behaviour,
Seductions, loud parties and fights,
Had once again gained the police's attention,
And soon they'd be reading their rights.

A spy by the name of Giovanni Manucci,
Was summoned to follow their flits,
To wheedle out info and log all the times,
The dandies were both off their tits.

Senator Bragadin who Casanova saved,
Had begged them to flee while they could,
The boys had to work off a hangover first,
But promised the next day they would.

But early that morn, the boys were arrested,
And thrown into jail without trial,
They were sentenced to 5 years for fooling around,
In a flea pit that really lacked style.

At Bragadin's insistence their cell was changed,
Warmer bedding and books they now had,
With a comfortable armchair placed by their beds,
It had turned to a reasonable pad.

On an exercise walk in the prison grounds,
A small iron bar they procured,
They smuggled it into the cell with great haste,
And into the armchair secured.

Casanova then sharpened the bar with a stone,
And under his bed he then dug,
But three days before their planned escape,
They were split into rooms that were snug.

His Chair with the bar was placed in his cell,
And he passed it to Phillatious next door,
"I think you can break through the ceiling" he said
"I've now given up with the floor."

Phillatious broke through and across to his friend,
Pulling him up through a hole,
They scaled the roof and broke through a window,
Then changed into clothes that they stole.

At the very last door, between freedom and them,
They spotted a guard with a truncheon,
They told him that they had been sadly locked in,
The previous night at a function.

As the guard let them out, they ran like the wind,
Then laughed and started to dance,
Then having collected their hideaway money,
They once again headed for France.

It was January 5th, 1757,
That to Paris the boys would now swing,
The very same day that Robert-Francois Damiens,
Had attempted to murder the King.

TRUNCHEON

BLUDGEON

STAFF

B BATTON

COSH

TOUGH

BILLY

BELL

BLACKJACK

STAFF

BILLY CLUB

LIFE PRESERVER

They once again needed to find a new patron,
So turned to Bernis, an old friend,
He had become the foreign minister of France,
So they'd have a few pennies to spend.

He told them they certainly had to gain favour,
Following all of their acts of the past,
To make the state money would certainly help,
To erase all the doubt pretty fast.

So they started as salesmen for a state lottery,
Selling tickets to people of wealth,
They soon became ever so good at the job,
And became pretty wealthy themselves.

High circles were once again prey for the boys,
And encounters with lovelies a must,
They breezed into socials and balls by the dozen,
And seemed to be gaining some trust.

When gracefully charming they mixed with the best,
And were no longer looked on as herberts,
They ate from the finest tables in house,
And thirstily downed many sherbets.

But along with the drink came the very tall tales,
With Casanova then claiming to be,
A spiritual alchemist and wizard of science,
Which the town folk had lapped up with glee.

Phillatious then claimed he was 300 years old,
And ladies would flock for his knowledge,
He claimed he could give them the secret of youth,
But first they should play with his sausage.

Casanova was loud with his spiritual chants,
And removing his clothes, a surprise,
He ripped off his shirt with incredible ease,
But needed some help with his flies.

Madame de Pompadour rushed to his aid,
And was quickly one of his quests,
He gallantly thanked her with a kiss on the hand,
Then quickly moved onto her guests.

This kind of behaviour had gone on for months,
And the boys had become quite enamoured,
But the trouble with partying 24-7,
Is they'd also become pretty hammered.

So Bernis then sent them to spy in Dunkirk,
Which was easy, and very well paid,
But the seven year war had started to grow,
So new planning then had to be made.

The state treasury needed to gain many funds,
So they had to sell bonds to the Dutch,
The boys went to Holland and did very well,
And to riches said 'Thanks very much.'

They founded a factory upon their return,
Producing the finest of silk,
Making quality clothing and the finest kerchiefs,
And all sorts of things of that ilk.

The French were elated and offered them titles,
And a pension for what they'd refined,
If they worked for the ministry as citizens of France,
An offer the boys both declined.

Sadly their business soon ran into debt,
And the boys became idle and shirkers,
They borrowed a lot but then blew all their dosh,
On liaisons with female co workers.

Madame Proufr

ALL SORTS OF PRETTY THINGS INSIDE

FINEST

FRENCH CAMBRIC FOUR PRETTY HANKIES 1/6

HANKIES

For debts they were once again sent to a prison,
At For-L'eveque, despite a strong plea,
But after four days the Marquise d'ufe,
Took pity and set the boys free.

Their patron De Bernis dismissed them from hand,
And they gained many troubles from foes,
So they sold their belongings and headed abroad,
Back to Holland to ease all their woes.

But this time they failed so they fled to cologne,
And in Stuttgart in 1760,
They lost all their fortune and were arrested once more,
For bad debts and being too frisky.

The boys were placed in a damp filthy cell,
With guards that ignored all their calls,
Their cellmate was a clown from the carnival hall,
Who liked to juggle his balls.

They had to escape from the sentence laid down,
As neither could serve the full maxi,
And they'd heard of dropping the soap on the floor,
And taking a hit up the Jacksy.

So they studied the staff and times they were moved,
Till one day they were ready to flee,
They said their goodbyes to the ball obsessed clown,
And made a mad dash to be free.

They managed to escape and headed down south,
And in Switzerland found some rest bite,
By this time the boys were knackered and broke,
And were hardly then able to fight.

They visited a Monastery at Einsiedeln,
And considered a new life as monks,
But felt it was selfish and wouldn't be right,
To deny all the girls of two hunks.

Besides that the hairstyle was not a good look,
Nor the fabric that made up the habits,
For surely their nethers would burst into flames,
From the friction when humping like rabbits.

Moving on they then visited Albrecht von Haller,
Voltare, Marseille and Genoa,
Then Florence, Modena, Naples and Rome,
From one sexual romp to another.

Phillatious decided to go by the name,
Of the Chevalier De Maison Von Quill,
Casanova himself was the Count D'Farussi,
And the two of them lived for the thrill.

In Rome they promoted the wide catholic faith,
And the Pope gave them medals of favour,
But having seduced the Pope's female aids,
Their popularity had started to waver.

England was next, where an audience was blagged,
With the head royal, King George the third,
But their lottery plans were dismissed out of hand,
As the King thought the whole thing absurd.

While living in England an apartment was let,
With an advert for ladies to share,
It said that they must have a liberal mind,
And preferably their own teeth and hair.

For many a time the girls came and went,
And were happy to serve their desire,
But acts such as this soon lead to disease,
As their meat and two veg were on fire.

They moved on to Belgium, both potless and ill,
And spent a few years getting well,
They travelled to many a country nearby,
And then stumbled on Russia as well.

Sadly they fought over girls with a Colonel,
And a duel with two pistols was planned,
Casanova would take on the foe himself,
And duly got shot in the hand.

The medics declared that the hand should come off,
And disclosed all their plans in a letter,
Philly and Cas told the docs to sod off,
And soon Casanova was better.

But Expelled from Warsaw they headed to France,
With Paris the City of Favour,
Phillatious again found his Jodie Bouteille,
And this time he wanted to savour.

But Jodie had accepted the hand of a fop,
Roberto, the Marquis D' Smarty,
He had all the wealth and was hung like a horse,
So Jodie could no longer Party.

Phillatious was crushed but wouldn't give up,
As he heard that her man was not brave,
Apparently power is all that he loved,
And he treated his girl like a slave.

So Philly and Cas would hatchet a plan,
To set up the fop with a girl,
He duly obliged and the union was done,
And Jodie was free in a whirl.

Phillatious would act as a shoulder to her,
As she cried for the love she must sever,
Of course what had happened could never come out,
Or Phillatious would lose her forever.

Jodie would stare at the Rogue's brownie eyes,
And could see the most loving of men,
She then whispered softly in the Rogue's longing ear,
That she thought he had shit himself again.

While Phillatious and Jodie were kindling their love,
Casanova was gambling once more,
He had many flings and his past was revealed,
So King Louis soon showed him the door.

Phillatious of course had a strong bond with Cas,
And suggested they all leave together,
But Jodie was not sure of leaving her France,
Would turn out to be very clever.

So Phillatious now had a decision to make,
Whether stay or to leave with his friend,
He decided he couldn't leave his mate in the lurch,
But promised to return in the end.

They headed for Spain where not so well known,
And attempted to schmooze with the rich,
They finally got to meet Charles the third,
But the King wasn't buying their pitch.

They stayed in a district Delmardo Borento,
Where just about anything goes,
They claimed they could offer the fountain of youth,
With simply one lick of their hose.

Barcelona was tricky and enemies grew,
As the lads ran around causing strife,
The men of the city were very upset,
And attempts were made on their life.

So around Spain they went with little success,
And money became very short,
With locals and ladies not feeling the love,
They headed on back to the port.

"We must change our lives" said Phillatious one day,
"They don't seem to understand fun,"
Casanova agreed with an audible sigh,
"I'm tired of being on the run."

So briefly they pondered and sneaked back to France,
Where Jodie this time left her home,
Phillatious had promised her nothing but love,
So the three of them headed for Rome.

Venice was really the home for the boys,
And in Rome they appealed their return,
They wrote to inquisitors, seeking permission,
But patience they needed to learn.

So during this time they wrote many things,
Casanova would write about Poland,
But also a comical play of the day,
Bout his fight with a farmer called Roland.

Phillatious and Jodie were writing a play,
Bout a man with a very long coat,
"I Know" said Jodie, "He could flash everyone,
Then get arrested for shagging a goat."

Phillatious stared at the love of his life,
As she smiled with delight from her chair,
Although she was pretty and very well formed,
He wondered if she was all there.

After all he remembered her kicking his nuts,
And standing there starting to laugh,
And the time that he passed out lacking from air,
When she tightened his neck with her scarf.

But he knew that's what made her the girl that she was,
And he loved all her nonsense and fun,
After all it was only that time with the poker,
That he'd felt that he needed to run.

Their supporters in Venice were working quite hard,
To procure them return to the state,
They said the authorities needed some help,
And some spying for them would be great.

Jodie was happy to join in with work,
And to spying she seemed quite a natural,
She came up with info that blew the states mind,
And some of it even seemed factual.

The boys too would gather up hearsay and gossip,
So to dance to the beat of their drum,
Then in the year of our lord 1774,
The letter had finally come.

The lads had been granted permission to return,
After 18 years banned from their home,
The three of them packed up their items in haste,
Then smiling, bid farewell to Rome.

They were treated like celebs upon their return,
With a handshake and plenty of ale,
Even the inquisitors had wanted to know,
How the two of them had escaped from their jail.

One of the inquisitors was Danddo by name,
A Fop, and a bit of a mouse,
But welcomed the guests with wide open arms,
And said they could live at his house.

Not being shy they jumped at the chance,
And writing for him they were willing,
The play with the goat had earned a few bucks,
But they needed to earn a real living.

While Phillatious and Jodie were writing Goat 2,
Casanova was earning from spying,
Writing reports on religion and Commerce,
From Gossip and generally lying.

But the nights in the city were always a hoot,
With the three of them rarely off form,
The nobles and toffees were in for a shock,
When they hit all the socials by storm.

Phillatious and Jodie were drinking like fish,
With a Spanish wine tipple called Dulce,
Casanova had grown an insatiable lust,
And would knob anything with a pulse.

One night on the lash Phillatious was shocked,
When Jodie had flashed him an eyeful,
He suddenly tripped, fell arse over tit,
And ended face down in a trifle.

His girl laughed so hard she fell over backwards,
Breaking a table and chair,
The nobles all gasped as they stared at the sight,
Of her lying with her bum in the air.

"I am a lady!" she shouted out loud,
When standing and straightening her dress,
"Although at this moment I have to concede,
I'm looking a bit of a mess."

"Nonsense," yelled Phillatious, covered in cream,
As two drinks he started to pour,
They sank them straight back and started to laugh,
Then once again fell on the floor.

Casanova then helped them to regain their feet,
With the help of an old wooden broom,
And so then began the 3 hour climb,
Up the 8 steps that lead to their room.

They sang all the way about Nobles and Fops,
And dandies with wigs on their head,
Then finally crawled through the door of their room,
And both fell face down on the bed.

Casanova had checked them, then gone to his room,
Where a girl called Francesca was waiting,
They fondled and cuddled then both fell asleep,
But soon it was her, he was dating.

But all of the parties were taking their toll,
And money was soon to get tight,
All of their writings were not selling well,
And the future was not looking bright.

While feeling quite low Phillatious was shocked,
By the news of the death of his mum,
Then the illness of his friend, Cortina Guzzi,
Who had once fingered his bum.

He went to Cortina who lay on her deathbed,
She grinned at the sight of his charms,
He gave her a kiss and a loving farewell,
As she smiled and then died in his arms.

Casanova and Jodie would join their friend Philly,
At a hostelry close to the city,
They drank to the loved ones and toasted their lives,
But none of them wallowed in pity.

For life was too short and enjoy it you must,
And money for them was the key,
Casanova had published his books on the Polish,
And his friends had now started Goat 3.

But sales were low and other plans failed,
Francesca was now off the scene,
Phillatious and Jodie had run out of booze,
And were no longer living the dream.

Casanova's writings then poked fun at nobles,
Whose punishment upon them was stern,
They once again banned all three from the city,
And this time they'd never return.

They went back to Paris in 1783,
Where Phillatious would meet Jodie's family,
And ask for the hand of the love of his life,
From her father, a bruiser named Stanley.

But Stanley was rigid and disliked the Quill,
And wanted to put him to the test,
Meanwhile Casanova was schmoozing his wife,
And at one point was fondling her breast.

"You say that you love her" Stanley began,
But to me there is only one way,
You must drop the Surname you got from your dad,
And become Phillatious Bouteille.

Phillatious was angry at Stanley's suggestion,
For despite his own parents' dismiss,
He was a Quill and proud of his name,
And Stanley was taking the piss.

"How dare you!" said Philly, "My name is my Name,
I will not assume any other,
As Cas and I learnt at the lodge in Lyon,
A brother will fight for a brother.

Stanley was shocked, but grinned at the rogue,
For he too was also a mason,
"Forgive me Phillatious" he said with a smile,
This Marriage is something to hasten.

The Wedding was arranged at St Etienne Du Mont,
A church with a lavishing history,
The train of the dress was 50 yards long,
Which to this day is somewhat a mystery.

As Jodie walked past she pulled down a table,
And others would trip on the cloth,
Phillatious himself went arse over tit,
And the vicar was tied up in knots.

But the service went well, with Cas as best man,
And the vicar declared they were married,
They both then collapsed from the pre wedding booze,
And out of the church they were carried.

The party to follow was held at the Manor,
With Stanley in charge of his aides,
And Cas with a speech that would curl your toes,
About him and his friend's Escapades.

Ladies were fainting as Casanova spoke,
Of conquests the two friends had counted,
Plus all of the japes and the larking around,
And all of the ladies they'd mounted.

Then followed the dancing and drinking of wine,
And a cake fight with sponge in the air,
Stanley soon realised his life was to change,
As he laughed at the loveable pair.

That night in the boudoir, as husband and wife,
Phillatious and Jodie had kissed,
They wanted to make love like never before,
But quite frankly were too bloody pissed.

At one point Casanova came stumbling in,
A girl in each arm to deposit,
He asked his two friends to watch them a while,
While he took a pee in the closet.

"My dear friend Phillatious," said Cas with a grin,
His todger still out of his pants,
"I love you both dearly, and know that your lust,
Will somehow develop romance."

Phillatious And Jodie thanked their dear friend,
As he left with his ladies in tow,
"That man's like my brother" said Philly with love,
"I really don't want him to go."

But Cas had secured a very good job,
In Vienna, for Sebastian Farscarini,
It paid very well, and with maids on the scene,
He was certain to romp with his weeny.

So upon the next morn, the friends did embrace,
And were truly the closest of men,
But as Cas walked away he hadn't a clue,
He would never see Philly again.

Phillatious Quill, would write many plays,
About love and the life as a dandy,
He recounted the stories that he and Cas had,
From notes that he kept that were handy.

Like the time, the boys had encountered a princess,
And invited her back for some tipples,
Then after a flirt and a hand up the skirt,
They were licking champagne off her nipples.

Or the time they had challenged Sally the soak,
To a drinking contest at 'The Bell',
By a quarter to 4 they were flat on the floor,
And she nicked both their wallets as well.

Jodie was loving and very supportive,
Till one day she said, "I feel Funny,
I've felt pretty sick for a couple of days,
And there's wriggling about in my tummy."

The couple rejoiced as the baby news spread,
And Jodie said "Thank god for that,
With all of the drinking and eating I've done,
I thought I was just getting fat."

"Oh my darling Jodie" Phillatious proclaimed,
With your weight I can promise you this,
It would bother me not, if you doubled in size,
But any more, you'd be taking the piss.

So several months later the family cheered,
As Jodie gave birth to a son,
Phillatious didn't care that his boy had no hair,
Or that Jodie now weighed half a ton.

He was full of rejoice and wept at the sight,
Of his beautiful wife with a child,
He knew it was time to become a great dad,
And no longer live life so wild.

Of course they could still have a whole lot of fun,
With drinking and laughs all the way,
But each day could look at the family they'd made,
And never have reason to stray.

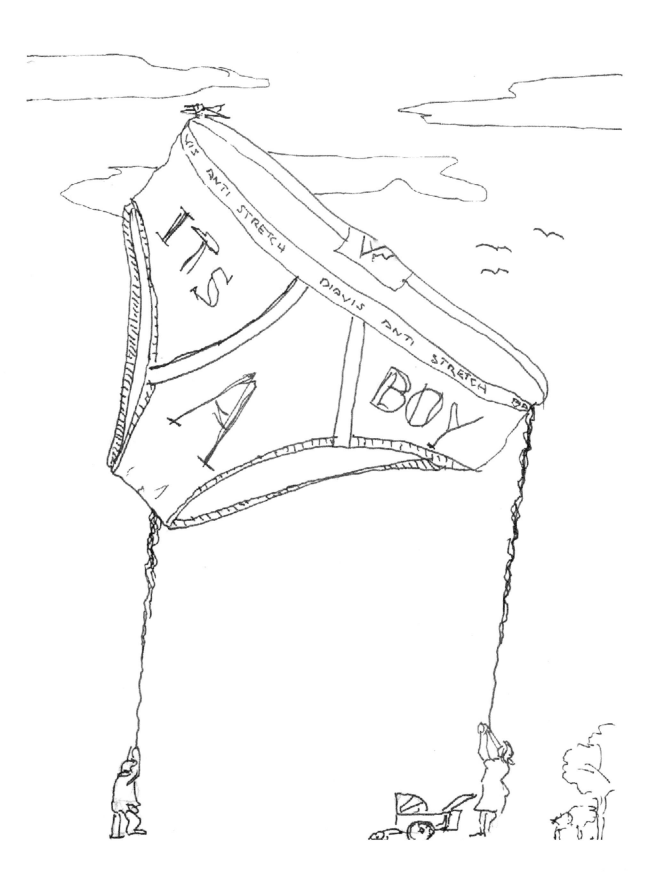

As the years passed on by, Phillatious was calm,
With family and friends he could trust,
He no longer felt the need to meet girls,
And bury his face in their bust.

Nor did he feel the need to strip off,
And run round flashing his hardwood,
Plus he knew if he fancied a bit on the side,
Then Jodie would cut off his manhood.

Phillatious just smiled with his son at his side,
And beckoned his wife to come over,
He gave her a kiss and they talked for a while,
Of their memories of dear Casanova.

On the grapevine, Phillatious had heard that his friend,
Had moved to the land of Bohemia,
And worked in the library of Count Von Waldstein,
In a job that could hardly be easier.

Apparently he lived at the Castle of Dux,
Writing his memoirs for print,
He'd visited Prague and encountered the King,
And had written some plays for a stint.

But sadly his health was not very good,
And he grew very bored at the castle,
He longed for the days he recounted in text,
When being a rogue and a rascal.

On the 4th of June 1798,
Giacomo Casanova passed away,
"I have lived as a philosopher, and I die as a Christian,"
Were the very last words he would say.

Phillatious and Jodie would hear of the news,
And travelled to Dux for a while,
They saw where the nobles had buried their friend,
And were told he was wearing a smile.

They joined all the locals and went to a hostel,
And told many tales of his life,
"You don't have to tell me," said a man at the bar,
"I caught him in bed with my wife."

The locals all laughed, but Phillatious consoled,
That his wife must indeed be a beauty,
For only the fairest of maidens could make,
His friend Casanova feel fruity.

Of course this had been a bit of a lie,
But Phillatious was trying to wag it,
The truth is that Cas had a motto in life,
If it moved, he would probably shag it.

So back home to Paris the couple returned,
Their travelling days were now over,
They went to the church and said a few prayers,
For the life of their friend Casanova.

Phillatious would live for 7 years more,
His son was a handsome young man,
They'd named him Giacomo, after their friend,
But his own life was carefully planned.

Phillatious and Jodie had lived and they'd laughed,
And enjoyed every moment together,
And as he was finally laid to his rest,
She told him she'd love him forever.

Phillatious had told her, he'd go and find Cas,
And one day would come say hello,
Jodie hadn't really believed in these things,
But it helped her to smile through the woe.

Till one day she stared, outside from her kitchen,
And was feeling a little in limbo,
When two little birds flew down from the sky,
And landed in front of her window.

She stared at them smiling then called for her son,
Who equally shared her delight,
The 2 little birds appeared to be talking,
A truly incredible sight.

They circled the garden a couple of times,
Then using their beaks as two pickers,
They swooped at her washing that hung on the line,
And quickly flew off with her knickers.

Jodie then laughed like never before,
And cuddled her smiling young lad,
"Only 2 creatures would pull such a stunt,
It was certainly Cas and your Dad."

They then raised a glass to toast the two birds,
Who had given them both, such a thrill,
"This is to Cas," said Jodie with a tear,
"And to my darling, Phillatious Quill."

THE END.

Phillatious Quill
Wordsearch

Find the following words in the grid below:-

Cockwaffle   **Boobies**   **Jacksy**   **Dandy**
Truncheon   **Fop**   **Brothel**   **Munter**   **Prick**
Bazooka   **Spitroast**   **Ballsack**   **Flange**
Bonus Word   **Twat**

```
T R U E L P J A C K S Y
G S E I B O O B J C L N
M P L H S Y R V D A P O
B I F X D N B K G S I E
A K F N U S C T P L F H
Z W A O L I J M W L W C
O D W V R E O U A A K N
O Y K P A F H N S B T U
K I C M D N G T Q C H R
A P O F J E Y E O N L T
R W C E K U L R X R Y V
B T S A O R T I P S B A
```

The Doubtful Tale Series
By
Mark Fribbens

cvdarts@hotmail.com
www.cvdarts.com

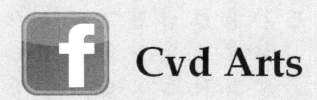 **Cvd Arts**

We very much hope you enjoyed
This publication and please look
Out for further 'Doubtful Tales'
Coming soon.

DOUBTFUL TALES DOUBTFUL TALES
DOUBTFUL TALES DOUBTFUL TALES
DOUBTFUL TALES DOUBTFUL TALES
DOUBTFUL TALES DOUBTFUL TALES
DOUBTFUL TALES DOUBTFUL TALES
DOUBTFUL TALES DOUBTFUL TALES
DOUBTFUL TALES DOUBTFUL TALES
DOUBTFUL TALES DOUBTFUL TALES
DOUBTFUL TALES DOUBTFUL TALES
DOUBTFUL TALES DOUBTFUL TALES
DOUBTFUL TALES DOUBTFUL TALES
DOUBTFUL TALES DOUBTFUL TALES
DOUBTFUL TALES DOUBTFUL TALES
DOUBTFUL TALES DOUBTFUL TALES
DOUBTFUL TALES DOUBTFUL TALES

DOUBTFUL TALES DOUBTFUL TALES
DOUBTFUL TALES DOUBTFUL TALES
DOUBTFUL TALES DOUBTFUL TALES
DOUBTFUL TALES DOUBTFUL TALES
DOUBTFUL TALES DOUBTFUL TALES
DOUBTFUL TALES DOUBTFUL TALES
DOUBTFUL TALES DOUBTFUL TALES
DOUBTFUL TALES DOUBTFUL TALES
DOUBTFUL TALES DOUBTFUL TALES
DOUBTFUL TALES DOUBTFUL TALES
DOUBTFUL TALES DOUBTFUL TALES
DOUBTFUL TALES DOUBTFUL TALES
DOUBTFUL TALES DOUBTFUL TALES
DOUBTFUL TALES DOUBTFUL TALES
DOUBTFUL TALES DOUBTFUL TALES

Printed in Great Britain
by Amazon

23164644R00059